D1362125

ISBN # 0-9760129-2-8
Library of Congress Control Number: 2004110957

Printed in China
First Edition, 2004
Edited by Mary Thomas
Photographs by KC Photography

Avant Garde Publishing

This book is not intended to provide
health advice. Consult with your
health care professional.

This book belongs to

Hi! My name is Apollo.
I'm a Saint Bernard.

I live with my pet, Mom Maw.

She named me Apollo after some Greek guy who was handsome and noble. She said I would grow up to be handsome and noble too.

Mom Maw was right!

I am very busy helping Mom Maw take care of her grandkids.

I met the two Big Ones first at the place where I was born. They called me a baby name, "Waddles." They said I waddled when I walked. HUH! At least my hips don't swing like the one with the hair like curly noodles.

They don't look like kids to me, but that is what Mom Maw calls them.

When I was just a puppy, I met My Boy. He came with Mom Maw and two of his sisters to see me at the place where I was born.

We had such fun that day.

I thought they would take me home with them, but they didn't.

The very next week, Mom Maw brought me home to live with her. When I got there, I found out that My Boy lives next door.

I was just
    an adorable, fluffy,
        little ball of fur, then.

Mom Maw said so!

I began to grow.....

and GROW...

and GROW!

I don't know why, but things seem to be getting smaller. There isn't even enough room in my chair for My Boy to sit with me anymore.

He will have to find somewhere else to sit.

The people seem to be getting smaller too.

It's hard to be a lap dog, when their laps keep shrinking.

I have a nice, big yard where I live. It is lots of fun to play in the yard with the kids.

Sometimes I leave my yard and go for a ride in the car with The Man.

I LOVE riding in the car.

It's my turn to drive now.
    OK?
        Huh?
            OK?

I work really hard helping Mom Maw teach the grandkids good health habits.

Drinking lots of water is very important. Water flushes toxins out of your body.

It is best to drink at least eight glasses of water a day.

Isn't Mom Maw sweet to leave a drink for me in her good crystal glass? It's usually full of flowers.....

Mom Maw tells the grandkids to eat lots of fresh vegetables every day. Vegetables and fruits give you vitamins and minerals.

I set a good example by fixing my own salad.

Then, Mom Maw says flowers are really NOT salad.

Salad is made from plants, isn't it?

Staying clean washes away germs and lets your skin breathe. It makes you smell nice too.

I make sure the kids get a good bath.

Bubbles
All
Over
The
House!

Exercise helps muscles grow strong.
I give the kids a lot of exercise.

I take them for walks....

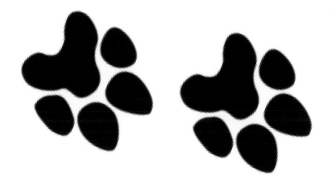

I play wrestle with My Boy.

I always win!

I play games with them like

TUG-G-O-WAR.

It's my favorite. I win that too!

My next most favorite game is
Tag-You're It.

Ha! I won again!

I teach them good manners too...

like SHARING!

I guess he needs to have a few more lessons.

After a long, hard day, it's time to settle down and rest. Resting gives your body time to cleanse inside.

I love these quiet moments, but these concrete steps are hard.

This comfy bed is more like it.

A good night's sleep is one good health habit I really go for. I like eight hours or more with a little nap or two during the day.

Taking care of all these kids is very tiring...

zZ Z   zZ Z   zZ Z

OH
NO!
A new one!

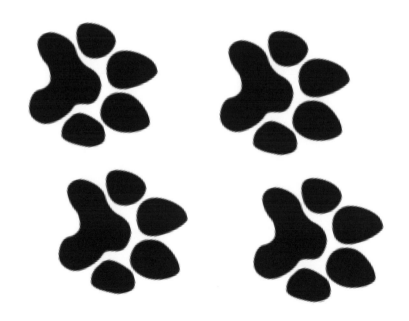

Kid's Healthy Snacks

1 cup butter, softened	2 cups raw sugar or fructose
2 eggs	1/2 cup honey
2 tsp. pure vanilla	2 tsp. cinnamon
1 1/2 cup unbleached flour	1 1/2 cup whole wheat flour
1 cup oats (optional)	1 tsp. SynerProTein*
1/2 tsp. Berry Healthy*	2 tsp. aluminum-free baking powder

In a medium bowl, cream together butter and sugar, add eggs, honey and vanilla. Set aside. In a large bowl, sift together flour, baking powder and cinnamon. Stir in SynerProTein and Berry Healthy. Fold in sugar mixture and oats.

Roll out on a floured surface. Cut out shapes with cookie cutters (we used bone shaped cookie cutters). Place on cookie sheet and bake at 350 degrees for 9 to 12 minutes. Cool before eating.

*SynerProTein is an excellent source of protein from soy. It helps build strong bones. Berry Healthy is a powder made from berries which has anti-oxidant properties to boost the immune system. Both are available through Beth Fitzgerald, independent distributor at www.mynsp.com/fitzgerald1.

Use this recipe as is or make up your own version. Try different flavorings. The author's favorite is orange with no cinnamon. Experiment.
Recipe by Rhonda West.

This recipe has been kid-tested and approved. Look for more healthy recipes for kids in future Apollo books.....coming soon!

Apollo says, "Eat healthy and you could be as magnificent as me. Maybe!"

Kids enjoy helping make these healthy cookies in their favorite shapes--a great rainy day project.

Great for lunches, afterschool snacks or any time.

Apollo

By Rhonda West

Oh, there once was a fluffy little pup
who was just barely a lump.
He started out so small,
that you'd hardly notice him at all.
He couldn't even play,
He slept the whole day,
only waking long enough to chaw.

When at last he did wake,
he realized his mistake
of sleeping the whole day through.
For when he opened his eyes,
much to his surprise,
there were so many things to CHEW.

He wanted to explore all that he found,
so out of his yard he came with a bound.
Day by day he grew
and soon everyone knew if he were about,
they must watch out,
for he looked like a puppy no more.
On his hind legs he doth stand, as tall as a man,
reaching the height of 6'4".

The lady, you see, who owns this puppy,
with great effort she tried.
A fence was put around, under the ground,
to deliver a shock to his hide.
But the neighbors knew, there was no doubt,
once again, that pup would get out.

ORDER THIS BOOK

If you can't find this book in your local book-store, request it or order here.

I want _____ copies of Apollo and the Grandkids, Good Health Habits for $11.95 each.

Please include $3.95 for shipping and handling for one book and $1 for each additional book.

Payment must be included with order. Please allow 3 to 4 weeks for delivery.

Name: _____

Address: _____

_____

Phone: _____ Email: _____

Payment by: _____ Money Order ____ Credit Card

Card #: _____

Exp. Date: _____ Signature: _____

JBK Publishing - Division of Avant Garde Publishing
32 Carmen Lane
Greenup, KY 41144

Visit www.annshealthandwealth.com for advance notice of publishing date for more Apollo books.

This page may be copied to send order.